Total Solar Eclipse

A STELLAR FRIENDSHIP STORY

Written by **Jayme Sandberg**

Illustrated by **Kathleen Gadeken**

It's All Stories

To Nora and Molly, my Sun and Moon. — J.S.

To Hayden, Ben and Kate, may your light always shine brighter together. — K.G.

Copyright © 2023 Jayme Sandberg
First published in 2023 by It's All Stories LLC
Lincoln, NE

ItsAllStories.com

This book is an introduction to total solar eclipses through fiction storytelling. While every
effort has been made to responsibly convey the phenomenon and solar viewing safety, this
book is not intended as a substitute for professional advice on solar eclipse viewing or for
close adult supervision of children viewing a solar eclipse. The book creators and publisher do
not assume and hereby disclaim any liability to any party for any loss, damage, or disruption
caused by errors or omissions, whether from negligence, accident, or any other cause.

Library of Congress Control Number: 2023937709

ISBN: 979-8-9882841-1-6 paperback
ISBN: 979-8-9882841-0-9 hardback
ISBN: 979-8-9882841-2-3 ebook

Editing by Marsha Diane Arnold
Book Design by Michael Rohani

Special thanks to those who shared their expertise and support
along the way including Dr. Julie Read, John Jerit and the team at
American Paper Optics, and many others. Together we shine!

I'm usually a sunny sort of star, but today, I'm **totally** out of sorts.

Breaking this super-duper serious safety rule is enough to get my hydrogen gas sizzling.

But that's not even all.

One of my favorite
friends is to blame.

During the total solar eclipse, Moon will hide my light by playing a cosmic game of **peek-a-boo**.

Moon totally knows how to get in the way!

First, Moon will change my **shape** for hours during the day.

Shadows will start to look strange.

Then, there will be an **odd glow** and a **sunset** from every direction.

It will look like I've **disappeared.**

YIKES!

I love being the center
of our solar system. Earthlings say
I'm especially good at my extra important job.

Will Earthlings think less of me when my
light goes out in the daytime?
I need to learn more. I know who to ask.

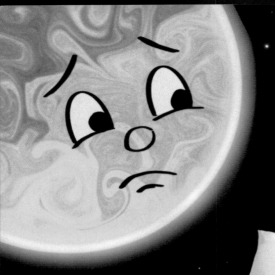

Earth sent a speedy reply.

My Forgetful Sun,

As I always say, my Earthlings know your safety rule and will protect their eyes when they look to the skies.

Your "friend" should write to Moon.

Gratefully yours,

Earth

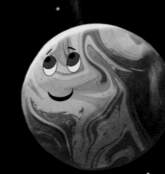

To my surprise,
I heard back quickly.

Hi Sun,

I've been expecting your letter. As I always say, Earthlings will think we're **both** totally stellar!

Try to chill and look forward to a spectacular show.

See you around,

Moon

Chill? What a laugh!

I'm always scorching hot.

Moon is obviously jealous

because I'm the star around here.

Oh no! I've barely had time to rise and shine and Moon is already moving in.

Millions of Earthlings are staring directly into my intense light!

Why aren't they getting hurt? What are those glasses everyone is wearing?

This is all very strange.

It's not *exactly* bad. It even looks a *little* fun.

I still have a serious sinking feeling about what's coming next.

You're really crowding me.

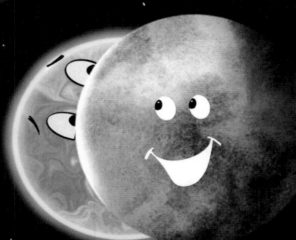

Do you have to be so close?

This is actually happening!

I don't believe what I'm hearing.

Earthlings **love** me in the dark!

In the full shadow of Moon during **totality**, they see my **solar corona.** I'm shining in a totally different way.

I need to see this for myself.

I'll take one tiny peek.

Earth was right.
Earthlings didn't get hurt.

Moon was right, too. We were
both stars today.

There's just one thing left to do.

Wait!

I have one more message.

It's for you, Earthling.

Dear Earthling,

I may forget things from time to time, but I was right about something from the beginning.

Looking directly at my bright light without a special filter like solar eclipse glasses is dangerous.

The only time it's okay to look at me without your solar eclipse glasses is during totality. That's when my disk is totally behind Moon. You'll know it's safe to take your eclipse glasses off when you can't see any part of me by looking through them.

When my bright light starts to peek out from behind Moon again—our diamond ring trick—you must put your eclipse glasses back on <u>right</u> <u>away</u>.

Protect your eyes when you look to the skies!

Your sincere star,

Sun

P.S. Each spot on Earth only has a total eclipse of me about once every 375 years. Capture your memories on the next page so you won't forget like me.

Total Solar Eclipse

My Name: _____

Date: _____ Where I was: _____

Who I was with: _____

How I felt: _____

What I want to remember: _____

_____

_____

_____

_____

_____

Glossary

Diamond ring effect (also called Baily's beads) – Something that happens at the very beginning and very end of totality when the last bit of sunlight sneaks through the Moon's uneven surface. The different size of the Moon's mountains and valleys makes one bright spot and lots of little dots around the Moon, which look like a diamond ring in the sky.

Moon – Earth's only natural satellite. The Moon keeps Earth from wobbling as much and is the reason there are ocean tides.

Solar corona – The white, outermost part of the Sun's atmosphere only visible during totality of a total solar eclipse. The Sun's corona is about 5 million miles high and is even hotter than the surface of the Sun.

Solar system – The group of planets, moons, and other objects orbiting a star.

Star – A huge ball of gas that gets bright and hot by burning hydrogen gas. The closest star to Earth is the Sun.

Sun – The only star in Earth's solar system. Without the Sun's light and warmth, there would be no life on Earth.

Totality – The moment during a total solar eclipse when the Moon is directly in front of the Sun, blocking its bright light.

Total solar eclipse (also called total eclipse of the Sun) – A rare event to see in the sky during the daytime where the Moon perfectly aligns between Earth and the Sun. From the places on Earth in the Moon's shadow, the Sun appears to disappear for up to several minutes.

Made in the USA
Monee, IL
10 January 2024

51555193R00021